THERE WERE 10 in the BED

and OTHER COUNTING Nursery RHYMES

Published by Bonney Press,
an imprint of Hinkler Books Pty Ltd
45–55 Fairchild Street
Heatherton Victoria 3202 Australia
www.hinkler.com.au

BONNEY
PRESS

© Hinkler Books Pty Ltd 2015

Illustrators: Steph Baxter, Sarah Coleman, Jon Contino, Sarah Dennis, Lauren Hom, Lalalimola,
Mick Marston, Jess Matthews, Chris Robertson, Marie Simpson, Alice Stevenson, Yulia Vysotskaya.

ISBN: 978 1 7436 3809 5

Printed and bound in China

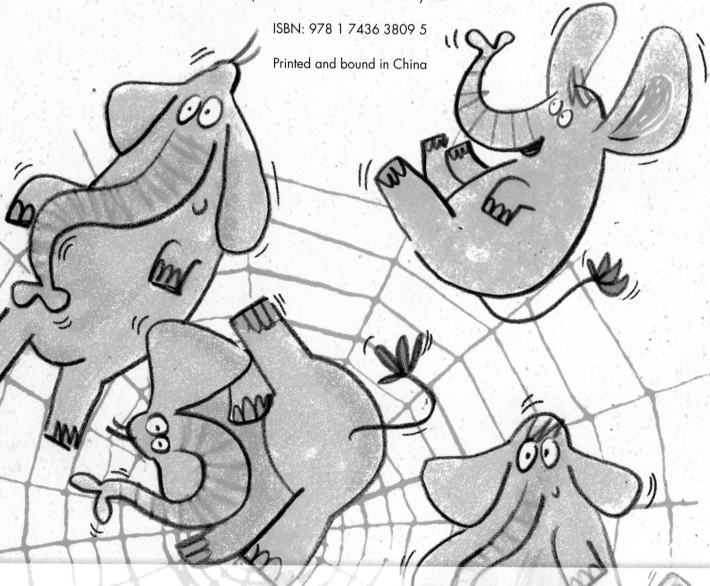

Contents

There were ten in the bed
And the little one said,
'Roll over! Roll over!'
So they all rolled over
And one fell out,
And he gave a little scream,
And he gave a little shout, 'Yahoo!'
Please remember to tie a knot in your pyjamas,
Single beds are only made for
One, two, three, four, five, six, seven, eight –

There were nine in the bed...
One, two, three, four, five, six, seven –

There were eight in the bed...
One, two, three, four, five, six –

There were seven in the bed...
One, two, three, four, five –

There were six in the bed...
One, two, three, four –

There were five in the bed...
One, two, three –

There were four in the bed...
One, two –

There were three in the bed...
One –

There were two in the bed
And the little one said,
'Roll over! Roll over!'
So they all rolled over
And one fell out,
And he gave a little scream,
And he gave a little shout, 'Yahoo!'
Please remember to tie a knot in your pyjamas,
Single beds are only made for one.
Single beds are only made for one.

10 GREEN BOTTLES HANGING ON THE WALL, TEN GREEN BOTTLES HANGING ON THE WALL, AND IF ONE GREEN BOTTLE SHOULD ACCIDENTALLY FALL, THERE'LL BE NINE GREEN BOTTLES HANGING ON THE WALL.

9 GREEN BOTTLES HANGING ON THE WALL, NINE GREEN BOTTLES HANGING ON THE WALL, AND IF ONE GREEN BOTTLE SHOULD ACCIDENTALLY FALL, THERE'LL BE EIGHT GREEN BOTTLES HANGING ON THE WALL.

8 GREEN BOTTLES HANGING ON THE WALL, EIGHT GREEN BOTTLES HANGING ON THE WALL, AND IF ONE GREEN BOTTLE SHOULD ACCIDENTALLY FALL, THERE'LL BE SEVEN GREEN BOTTLES HANGING ON THE WALL.

7 GREEN BOTTLES HANGING ON THE WALL, SEVEN GREEN BOTTLES HANGING ON THE WALL, AND IF ONE GREEN BOTTLE SHOULD ACCIDENTALLY FALL, THERE'LL BE SIX GREEN BOTTLES HANGING ON THE WALL.

6 GREEN BOTTLES HANGING ON THE WALL, SIX GREEN BOTTLES HANGING ON THE WALL, AND IF ONE GREEN BOTTLE SHOULD ACCIDENTALLY FALL, THERE'LL BE FIVE GREEN BOTTLES HANGING ON THE WALL.

5 GREEN BOTTLES HANGING ON THE WALL, FIVE GREEN BOTTLES HANGING ON THE WALL, AND IF ONE GREEN BOTTLE SHOULD ACCIDENTALLY FALL, THERE'LL BE FOUR GREEN BOTTLES HANGING ON THE WALL.

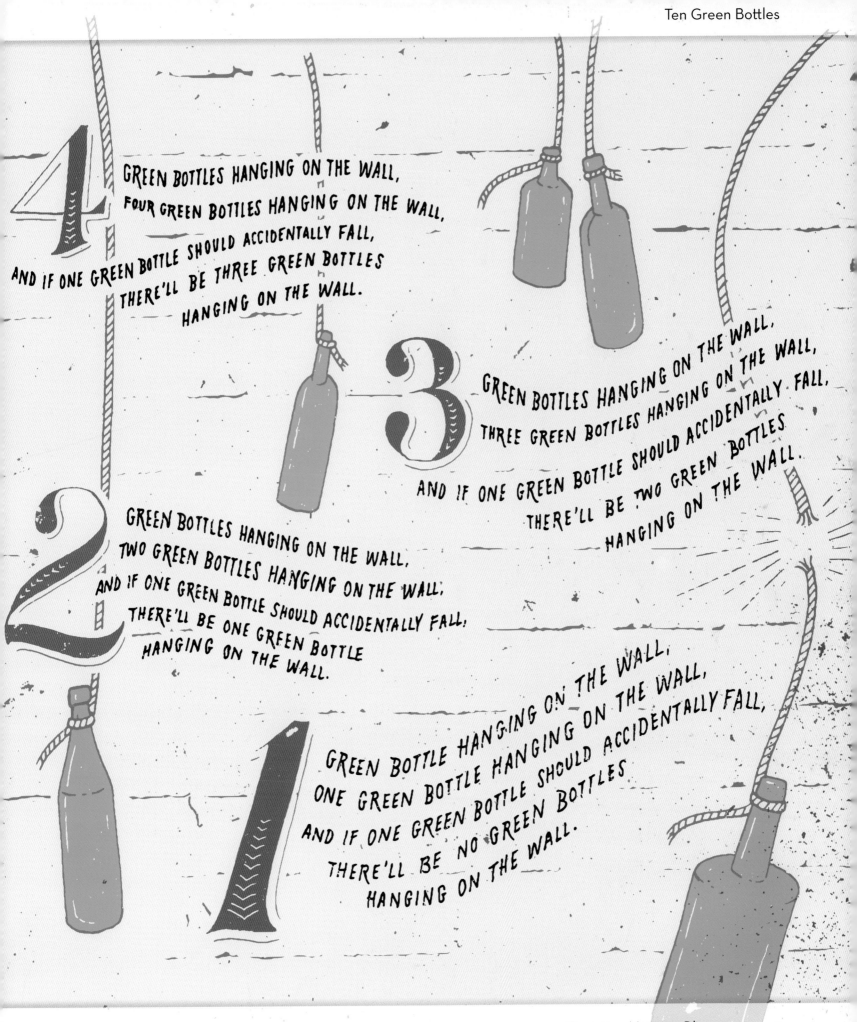

4 GREEN BOTTLES HANGING ON THE WALL,
FOUR GREEN BOTTLES HANGING ON THE WALL,
AND IF ONE GREEN BOTTLE SHOULD ACCIDENTALLY FALL,
THERE'LL BE THREE GREEN BOTTLES
HANGING ON THE WALL.

3 GREEN BOTTLES HANGING ON THE WALL,
THREE GREEN BOTTLES HANGING ON THE WALL,
AND IF ONE GREEN BOTTLE SHOULD ACCIDENTALLY FALL,
THERE'LL BE TWO GREEN BOTTLES
HANGING ON THE WALL.

2 GREEN BOTTLES HANGING ON THE WALL,
TWO GREEN BOTTLES HANGING ON THE WALL,
AND IF ONE GREEN BOTTLE SHOULD ACCIDENTALLY FALL,
THERE'LL BE ONE GREEN BOTTLE
HANGING ON THE WALL.

1 GREEN BOTTLE HANGING ON THE WALL,
ONE GREEN BOTTLE HANGING ON THE WALL,
AND IF ONE GREEN BOTTLE SHOULD ACCIDENTALLY FALL,
THERE'LL BE NO GREEN BOTTLES
HANGING ON THE WALL.

Chook, chook, chook-chook-chook,

Good morning Mrs Hen,

How many chickens have you got?

Madam, I've got ten.

Four of them are yellow,

And four of them are brown,

And two of them are speckled red,

The nicest in the town.

Five little monkeys,
Jumping on the bed;
One fell off
And bumped his head.
Mama called the doctor,
The doctor said:
'No more monkeys
Jumping on the bed!'

Four little monkeys,
Jumping on the bed…

Three little monkeys,
Jumping on the bed…

Two little monkeys,
Jumping on the bed…

One little monkey,
Jumping on the bed…

One, two, three, four, five,
Once I caught a fish alive;
Six, seven, eight, nine, ten,
Then I let it go again.

Why did you let it go?
Because it bit my finger so.
Which finger did it bite?
This little finger on the right.

THIS OLD MAN, HE PLAYED **1**

HE PLAYED KNICK~KNACK ON MY THUMB

CHORUS:

WITH A KNICK-KNACK

paddywhack

GIVE THE DOG A BONE

THIS OLD MAN CAME ROLLING HOME

this OLD MAN, HE PLAYED **2**

HE PLAYED knick-knack ON MY SHOE

CHORUS

THIS OLD MAN, HE PLAYED **3**

he played KNICK-KNACK on my knee

CHORUS

THIS OLD MAN, HE PLAYED **4**

HE PLAYED KNICK-KNACK on my DOOR

CHORUS

THIS OLD MAN, HE PLAYED 5 HE PLAYED KNICK~KNACK ON MY hive · CHORUS ·

this old man, HE PLAYED 6 HE PLAYED KNICK-KNACK ON MY STICKS CHORUS

THIS OLD MAN, HE PLAYED 7 HE PLAYED KNICK-KNACK UP IN HEAVEN CHORUS

THIS OLD MAN, HE PLAYED

8

HE PLAYED
knick-knack
ON MY GATE
CHORUS

this OLD MAN, *he played*

9

HE PLAYED
KNICK-KNACK
ON MY SPINE
CHORUS

THIS OLD MAN, HE PLAYED

10

he played
KNICK-KNACK
once again
· CHORUS ·

One elephant went out to play,
Upon a spider's web one day.
He had such enormous fun,
That he called for another elephant to come.

Two elephants went out to play,
Upon a spider's web one day.
They had such enormous fun,
That they called for another elephant to come.

Three elephants went out to play...

Four elephants went out to play...

Five elephants went out to play,
Upon a spider's web one day.
The web went creak, the web went crack,
And five elephants came running back!

Five little ducks went out one day
Over the hills and far away.
Mother duck said, 'Quack quack, quack quack!'
But only four little ducks came back.

Four little ducks went out one day
Over the hills and far away.
Mother duck said, 'Quack quack, quack quack!'
But only three little ducks came back.

Three little ducks went out one day
Over the hills and far away.
Mother duck said, 'Quack quack, quack quack!'
But only two little ducks came back.

Two little ducks went out one day
Over the hills and far away.
Mother duck said, 'Quack quack, quack quack!'
But only one little duck came back.

One little duck went out one day
Over the hills and far away.
Mother duck said, 'Quack quack, quack quack!'
But none of those five little ducks came back.

Mother duck she went out one day
Over the hills and far away.
Mother duck said, 'Quack quack, quack quack!'
And all of those five little ducks came back.

ONE, TWO, BUCKLE MY SHOE;
THREE, FOUR,
KNOCK on the door;
FIVE, SIX, PICK UP STICKS;
SEVEN, EIGHT,
LAY THEM STRAIGHT;
NINE, TEN,
A GOOD FAT HEN

ELEVEN, TWELVE,
DIG AND DELVE;
THIRTEEN, FOURTEEN,
MAIDS A-COURTING;
FIFTEEN, SIXTEEN,
MAIDS IN THE KITCHEN;
SEVENTEEN, EIGHTEEN,
MAIDS A-WAITING;
NINETEEN, TWENTY,
MY PLATE'S empty.

Three blind mice, three blind mice
See how they run! See how they run!
They all ran after the farmer's wife,
Who cut off their tails with a carving knife;
Did you ever see such a thing in your life,
As three blind mice?

The ants go marching one by one, hurrah, hurrah,
The ants go marching one by one, hurrah, hurrah,
The ants go marching one by one,
The little one stops to suck his thumb

Chorus:
And they all go marching down to the ground
To get out of the rain, BOOM! BOOM! BOOM!

The ants go marching two by two, hurrah, hurrah…
The little one stops to tie his shoe
Chorus

The ants go marching three by three, hurrah, hurrah…
The little one stops to climb a tree
Chorus

The ants go marching four by four, hurrah, hurrah…
The little one stops to shut the door
Chorus

The ants go marching five by five, hurrah, hurrah…
The little one stops to take a dive
Chorus

The ants go marching six by six, hurrah, hurrah…
The little one stops to pick up sticks
Chorus

The ants go marching seven by seven, hurrah, hurrah…
The little one stops to pray to heaven
Chorus

The ants go marching eight by eight, hurrah, hurrah…
The little one stops to shut the gate
Chorus

The ants go marching nine by nine, hurrah, hurrah…
The little one stops to check the time
Chorus

The ants go marching ten by ten, hurrah, hurrah…
The little one stops to say 'The End'
Chorus

5 Five currant buns in a baker's shop,
Round and **fat** with a cherry on top,
Along came a boy with a penny one day,
Bought a currant bun and took it away.

4 Four currant buns in a baker's shop,
Round and **fat** with a cherry on top,
Along came a girl with a penny one day,
Bought a currant bun and took it away.

3 Three currant buns in a baker's shop,
Round and **fat** with a cherry on top,
Along came a boy with a penny one day,
Bought a currant bun and took it away.

2 Two currant buns in a baker's shop,
Round and **fat** with a cherry on top,
Along came a girl with a penny one day,
Bought a currant bun and took it away.

1 One currant bun in a baker's shop,
Round and **fat** with a cherry on top,
Along came a boy with a penny one day,
Bought a currant bun and took it away.

One man went to mow,
Went to mow a meadow;
One man and his dog, Spot,
Went to mow a meadow.

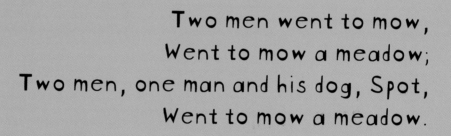

Two men went to mow,
Went to mow a meadow;
Two men, one man and his dog, Spot,
Went to mow a meadow.

Three men went to mow...

Four men went to mow...

Five men went to mow...

Six men went to mow...

Seven men went to mow...

Eight men went to mow...

Nine men went to mow...

Ten men went to mow...

One for sorrow
Two for joy
Three for a girl
Four for a boy
Five for silver
Six for gold
Seven for a secret
Never to be told